STUBBY & FRIENDS

WRITTEN BY SCOTT CHRISTIAN SAVA

ILLUSTRATED BY TRACY BAILEY

ISBN: 978-1-7356794-0-2
www.stubbysquad.com

EVERYONE! I WOULD LIKE TO INTRODUCE YOU TO MY AMERICAN FRIENDS!
THEY WILL BE STAYING WITH US HERE IN FRANCE FOR A WHILE.

ROBERT CONROY, SERGEANT STUBBY...
...PLEASE MEET COLETTE AND PIERRE.

STUBBY

I THINK THAT WENT AS WELL AS CAN BE EXPECTED.
IF ONLY ALL FOREIGN RELATIONS WENT SO WELL.
OUI! PERHAPS A BIT OF LICKING MIGHT HAVE PREVENTED THE WAR, NON?

SO. AMERICAN? WHAT BRINGS YOU HERE TO FRANCE?
STUBBY
THE GREAT WAR.
WAR? I DIDN'T KNOW DOGS WERE ALLOWED TO GO WITH HUMANS IN THE WAR!

WELL. TECHNICALLY THEY'RE NOT. I JUST KIND OF BROKE THE RULES. SNUCK IN WHEN NO ONE WAS LOOKING.
USED MY BOYISH CHARMS TO GET MY WAY.

YEP. HE'S AMERICAN.
INDEED.

SURELY YOU WOULD HAVE GONE WITH YOUR MASTER IF YOU COULD HAVE.
STUBBY
ME? GO TO WAR?

WHY WOULD I DO SOMETHING SO IDIOTIC WHEN I HAVE EVERYTHING I NEED RIGHT HERE?

FINE FRENCH FOOD. WARM FIRE TO NAP IN FRONT OF.

OKAY. MAYBE THE INTELLECTUAL REPARTEE IS A BIT LACKING...

'ELLO, CHAPS!
BENSON!

WHO'S THE NEW BLOKE?
SERGEANT STUBBY. HE'S FROM AMERICA.

THE COLONIES? LITTLE KNOWN FACT ABOUT AMERICA. IT WAS ORIGINALLY FOUNDED BY CORGIS.

HOW IS IT YOU WERE BROUGHT UP IN A UNIVERSITY AND LITERALLY CAME OUT DUMBER THAN PIERRE THE COUNTRY BUMPKIN?
STUBBY

I'LL HAVE YOU KNOW, MY GOOD LADY, THAT I WAS AT THE TOP OF MY CLASS IN CAMBRIDGE.
WOW! REALLY? THAT'S AMAZING.
BENSON'S *REALLY* SMART.
STUBBY

SIGH SLEEPING IN THE ATTIC ABOVE A CLASSROOM IS *NOT* THE TOP OF YOUR CLASS!

TECHNICALLY...
STUBBY
HE HAS A POINT...

STUBBY
I'M DONE HERE.

WHAT'S THAT SMELL?
AH. YOU SMELL **GASTON** AND HIS **COOKING**. HE IS THE BEST CHEF IN ALL OF FRANCE.

I WONDER IF HE CAN MAKE MY FAVORITE MEAL.
STUBBY

ANYTHING. HE IS A **MASTER CHEF**. WHAT WOULD YOU LIKE HIM TO COOK FOR YOU?

ARMY RATIONS, STRAIGHT FROM THE CAN!

ÊTES-VOUS FOU, CHIEN STUPIDE!?* YOU CAN NOT COMPARE ARMY RATIONS TO THE FINE CUISINE OF FRANCE!
STUBBY
*"ARE YOU INSANE, YOU STUPID DOG?!"

WHY NOT?
BBY

"WHY NOT?" THAT'S... THAT'S LIKE COMPARING THE MONA LISA TO A CHILD'S DRAWING. OR MOZART'S CONCERTOS TO A LULLABY. OR... OR...

YOU KNOW? IT'S ACTUALLY PRETTY GOOD.
INDEED. YOU REALLY SHOULD HAVE A TRY, MY DEAR.
STUBBY

PEASANTS. SIMPLETONS. ALL OF YOU!

IN FRANCE, WE GROW THE FOOD OURSELVES. THE FRENCH PRIDE THEMSELVES ON THE SIMPLE THINGS.

SIMPLY PUT, MY CANINE COMPATRIOTS, WHEN IT COMES TO COOKING, THE FRENCH ARE THE ELITE. THE BEST OF THE BEST. LE PINACLE!

AHEM. IF I MAY, MY DEAR COLETTE... THE BRITISH INVENTED THE ART OF FINE CUISINE. PEOPLE FROM ALL OVER THE WORLD--

...FLOCK TO OUR COUNTRY TO TASTE THE CULINARY--
BANGERS AND MASH.

...DELIGHTS OUR BRITISH CHEFS CREATE--
HAGGIS.

BLOOD. PUDDING.
POINT TAKEN.

BOUILLABAISSE! BOUILLABAISSE! BOUILLABAISSE!

BOOYAH-WHAT?
BOUILLABAISSE, MY DEAR. PIERRE'S FAVORITE.
STUBBY

BOUILLABAISSE! BOUILLABAISSE! BOUILLABAISSE!

WHAT'S IN IT?
STUBBY
AH. YOU HAVE FRESH CLAMS, LOBSTER, MONKFISH, SNAPPER, HALIBUT....

BOUILLABAISSE! BOUILLABAISSE! BOUILLABAISSE!

ESSENTIALLY THE ENTIRE CONTENTS OF THE OCEAN IN ONE POT.

BOUILLABAISSE!
BOUILLABAISSE!
BOUILLABAISSE!
BOUILLABAISSE!

REALLY, PIERRE. IT'S JUST FISH SOUP.
STUBBY

I MEAN... IT CAN'T BE *THAT*...

HOLY MACKEREL! THIS STUFF IS *AMAZING*!

LESS TALKING, MORE EATING, AMERICAN!

WHAT A GREAT DINNER
INDEED.
MAYBE WE CAN GO OUT FOR A WALK?
A *SPLENDID* IDEA, OLD CHAP!
STUBBY

ARE YOU COMING, COLETTE?

ME? *OUTSIDE*? WITH THE *FARM ANIMALS*?

WHUMP

DID SHE JUST FAINT?
YOU KNOW THE FRENCH. ALWAYS SO DRAMATIC.
STUBBY

BONJOUR.
AH! WHAT'S THAT?
THAT IS PAULETTE THE COW.

A... A COW? I HAD NO IDEA THEY WERE SO... SO BIG!
STUBBY

YOU'VE NEVER SEEN A COW BEFORE? WHERE DID YOU GET YOUR MILK?
I GREW UP IN THE CITY. WE GOT OUR MILK THE OLD-FASHIONED WAY...
STUBBY

FROM A BOTTLE!
STUBBY

BONJOUR.
WHAT? WHAT ARE THEY?

CHICKEN AND GEESE, MY FRIEND. THEY PROVIDE THE EGGS GASTON USES IN HIS BAKING.
STUBBY
PROVIDE? PROVIDE HOW?

WELL... THEY LAY THE EGGS EACH DAY, OF COURSE.

I THINK I'LL STICK WITH MY ARMY RATIONS FROM A CAN.
STUBBY

I WOULD SHOW YOU THE ***GOATS*** NEXT, BUT NO ONE LIKES THEM.
OH? WHY NOT?

WHACK

THEY'RE ALWAYS *BUTTING* INTO CONVERSATIONS.

I DON'T BELIEVE THE AMERICAN GOT THE *POINT* OF YOUR JOKE, PIERRE.

OH... WE'RE JUST ABOUT GETTING TO THE *PUNCHLINE*, BENSON.

BACK SO SOON FROM YOUR TOUR OF THE FARM?

ALAS, MADAME, IT SEEMS OUR AMERICAN FRIEND DOES NOT AGREE WITH THE OPEN AIR AND FRENCH COUNTRYSIDE.

IT SEEMS THE FRENCH COUNTRYSIDE MAY NOT AGREE WITH HIM, AS WELL.

LET'S JUST AGREE TO DISAGREE... AND NEVER GO OUT THERE AGAIN. *AGREED?*
STUBBY

AGREED.

LOVED HOW YOU HANDLED THAT GOAT THERE, OL' CHAP!
WELL, YOU LEARN A THING OR TWO ABOUT FIGHTING IN THE ARMY, BENSON.
STUBBY

I BELIEVE I'D DO QUITE WELL IN THE ARMY. YES INDEED.
REALLY? YOU WANT TO GO TO WAR?
STUBBY

WAR? HEAVENS, NO!

I JUST THINK I'D LOOK SMASHING IN UNIFORM. DON'T YOU THINK?
STUBBY

AH, YES. I WOULD BE THE TALK OF THE TOWN.

THE LADIES LOVE A DOG IN UNIFORM.

KIDS WOULD IDOLIZE ME.

I WOULD LEAD PARADES...

OUI. YOU WOULD LEAD THEM RIGHT TO THE FUNNY FARM, YOU CRAZY CORGI.

I WOULD BE A FLYING ACE PILOT!
A TERROR IN THE SKIES.

THAT'S THE ROYAL AIR FORCE. NOT THE ARMY.
STUBBY

WELL, THEN I WOULD CAPTAIN A SHIP FOR A GREAT SEA BATTLE WHERE--

ROYAL NAVY. NOT THE ARMY.
STUBBY

WELL, WHAT DOES THE ARMY DO?

MAINLY SIT IN FOXHOLES AND EAT RATIONS FROM A CAN.
STUBBY

DESPITE THESE MINOR SETBACKS, I STILL BELIEVE I WOULD MAKE AN *EXCELLENT* ADDITION TO THE *ROYAL ARMY*!

AND I WOULD BE A LIFE-SAVING *NURSE*!

THE *U.S. ARMY* WOULD FIGHT BY YOUR SIDE.

AND THE *FRENCH SPACE CORPS* WILL PROTECT US ALL!

SPACE CORPS?

WELL... YEAH. TO PROTECT US FROM THE MOON MEN AND WHATNOT.

MAYBE I'M NOT CUT OUT FOR THE ROYAL ARMY ANYHOW.
IT'S PROBABLY FOR THE BEST, BENSON.
STUBBY
YOU'RE A SMART DOG. YOU COULD PUT THAT BIG BRAIN TO BETTER USE.

BUT IT *IS* A SHAME, THOUGH. TRULY A SHAME.
WHY, BENSON?

I REALLY THINK I WOULD HAVE LOOKED SMASHING IN THAT UNIFORM.
LADIES JUST LOVE A DOG IN UNIFORM.

AS A REPRESENTATIVE OF ALL FEMALES IN THE WORLD, BENSON, LET ME SAY...

...I THINK WE'LL GET OVER OUR DISAPPOINTMENT.

MON DIEU! WHAT IS THAT SMELL?!

SMELL?
I LIKE SMELLS!
WHAT SMELL?

OH! I SMELL IT NOW. IT'S COW.
NO NO NO. IT'S GOAT.
MY GOOD CHAPS. IT'S OBVIOUSLY GOOSE!

EEP!
STUBB
YES. DEFINITELY GOOSE.

AU SECOURS!
I AM ABDUCTED!
DID YOU
HEAR THAT?
COLETTE?

SHE'S GONE!
SHE'S BEEN
KIDNAPPED!
HELP!

TECHNICALLY
CAT-NAPPED.
OR A
KITTY CAPER?
MAYBE
IT'S A
FELINE
FELONY?

STOP CHARACTERIZING
MY ABDUCTION AND
SAAAAAVVVVE MEEEEEE!!!!!

OH NO!!
NOT THAT!!!
COLETTE!
I'M TOO
YOUNG! TOO
BEAUTIFUL!!!
WHERE
ARE YOU?
OH, THE
HORROR!
WE'LL
SAVE
YOU!
I AM DYING!
I AM DEAD!

OH NO! ARE YOU REALLY DEAD, COLETTE?
YES. I AM QUITE DEAD.

THAT DOESN'T MEAN YOU CAN STOP SAVING ME!

SEE, MY DEAR COLETTE? ALL DONE!
IT WAS JUST A BATH TO GET RID OF THAT HORRIBLE SMELL.

COLETTE!
STUBBY

DON'T LOOK AT ME! I AM DEFILED! I AM A MONSTER!

I NEARLY DROWNED!
THIS WAS YOUR GREAT DISASTER, MY DEAR? A BATH?
I WAS DYING!
OH, POOR KITTY!

HAHAHAHAHAHAHAHAHA
STUBBY

WELL. SINCE YOU ARE ALL HERE... INTO THE BATH YOU GO!

THAT'S WHAT WE GET FOR TRYING TO SAVE A CAT.
I DECLARE CHIVALRY OFFICIALLY DEAD.
NO GOOD DEED GOES UNPUNISHED.

YOU DIDN'T SAVE ME FROM THE BATH, *MES GARÇONS,* BUT YOU TRIED VALIANTLY.

YOU ARE MY HEROES.

WELL, NEXT TIME YOU GET A BATH, LADY... YOU'RE ON YOUR OWN.

WHAT'S WRONG, STUBBY?

I... I JUST MISS HOME.
STUBBY

HOME? IN AMERICA?

YEAH. CONNECTICUT. WHERE I GREW UP.

MY HOME IS OUT THERE IN THE WEST!

THAT WAY IS CHINA, MON AMI. YOU'RE FACING EAST.

WHAT'S AMERICA LIKE, SERGEANT STUBBY?
STUBBY
OH. IT'S BUSY. LOTS OF MACHINES. FACTORIES. PEOPLE.

AND CARS.
STUBBY

CARS?

HUMANS DRIVE THEM EVERYWHERE IN AMERICA.
STUBBY
BUT... WHAT ARE THEY GOOD FOR?

CHASING!
STUBBY

WHAT WAS YOUR HOME LIKE IN CONNECTICUT?
OH. HOME?
I... I DIDN'T REALLY HAVE ONE, BENSON.

NO HOME? TRÈS TRISTE! THAT IS NO WAY TO GROW UP!

IT WASN'T SO BAD. THERE WERE GARBAGE CANS FULL OF FOOD AT NIGHT.
STUBBY

YOU ATE TRASH?
WHEN I COULD FIND IT.

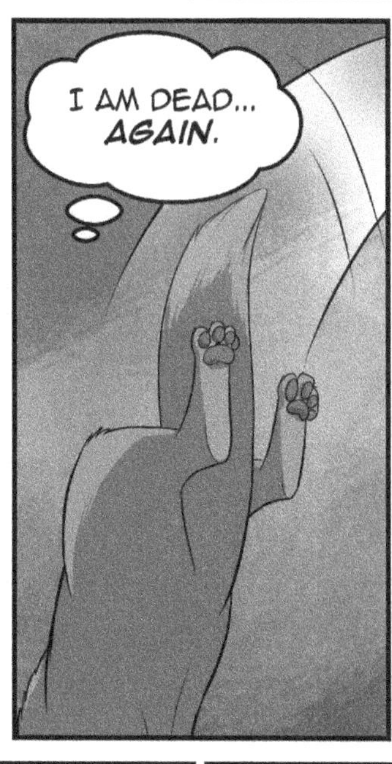
I AM DEAD... AGAIN.

OH, COLETTE. IT WASN'T SO BAD BEING ON THE STREETS.
ESPECIALLY WHEN I GOT TO TRY A NEW INVENTION MADE IN AMERICA.

AN INVENTION? WHAT KIND OF INVENTION?

PIZZA!
STUBBY

PIZZA? WHAT'S THAT?

IMAGINE A WARM BREAD COVERED IN SWEET TOMATO SAUCE AND DRIPPING WITH SOFT GOOEY CHEESE ON TOP.
STUBBY

THAT... THAT LITERALLY SOUNDS LIKE HEAVEN!

I WANT TO GO TO AMERICA AND TRY PIZZA!
IT DOES INDEED SOUND INTRIGUING.

PIZZA IS A NEW INVENTION FROM NEW YORK.
BUT NOW WE HAVE IT IN CONNECTICUT AND IT'S LIKE NOTHING I'VE EVER EATEN.

WELL... TO BE FAIR... YOUR ONLY COMPARISON COMES FROM THE GARBAGE.

STUBBY

TRUE.
STUBBY

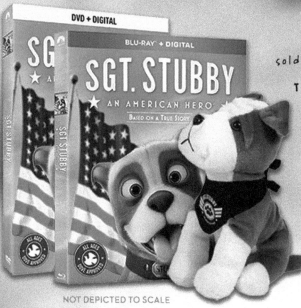

BOOK COMING SOON, BUT READ THE STORY AND TRY THE RECIPES TODAY AT WWW.STUBBYSQUAD.COM

WHAT IS THAT?

OH! IT'S HAPPENING!

IT'S *HERE!* IT'S *HERE!*

WHAT'S HERE, PIERRE?
WHAT IS THE MATTER?
STUBBY

THE PARADE! **THE PARADE!**

YOU HAVE PARADES IN THIS LITTLE TOWN?
OF COURSE! OF COURSE! IT'S THE BEST DAY OF THE YEAR!
STUBBY

NO FIRETRUCKS. NO CLOWNS. NO ACROBATS OR MOVIE STARS.
STUBBY

THIS IS ***NOTHING*** LIKE THE PARADES WE HAVE BACK HOME. WHAT MAKES IT SO SPECIAL, PIERRE?
STUBBY

TREATS FOR EVERYONE!

TREATS! TREATS! TREATS! TREATS!

TREATS! TREATS! TREATS! TREATS!

UM. SHOULD WE GO GET HIM?
STUBBY

OH, NO, NO, **NO**. THERE IS ***NOTHING*** WE CAN DO FOR ***POOR PIERRE***.
IT'S TRUE, MY LAD. HE'S IN THE CLUTCHES OF THE ***PARADE TREATS FRENZY***. TRAGIC, REALLY.

HE IS A LOST SOUL. HE WILL BE MISSED.

THIS IS CRAZY! I'VE GOT TO DO SOMETHING.
STUBBY

HANG IN THERE, PIERRE! I'LL SAVE YOU FROM YOUR PARADE TREATS FRENZY!

STUBBY
PARADE TREATS FRENZY?
IS THAT REALLY A THING?

PIERRE! YOU'RE OKAY! YOU SURVIVED THE PARADE TREATS FRENZY?

OF COURSE! I SURVIVED THE PARADE TREATS FREN...

BUT JUST BARELY, MON AMI.
BURP!

WHAT SAVED YOU?

THEY... THEY RAN OUT OF TREATS.
STUBBY

WHAT THE--?
EEP!
ZNORT!

WHAT HAPPENED?
I HAVE NO IDEA...
STUBBY

GOOD AFTERNOON, LADIES.
SO NICE OF YOU TO JOIN US FOR TEA.

TEA? WHAT'S TEA?
SMELLS FUNNY.

HOW DO YOU NOT KNOW ABOUT TEA, STUBBY?

I CAN UNDERSTAND THE FRENCH AND THEIR BOORISH WINE NOT KNOWING...BUT A ***COLONIST*** UNEDUCATED IN THE DELIGHTS OF TEA? BARBARIC.

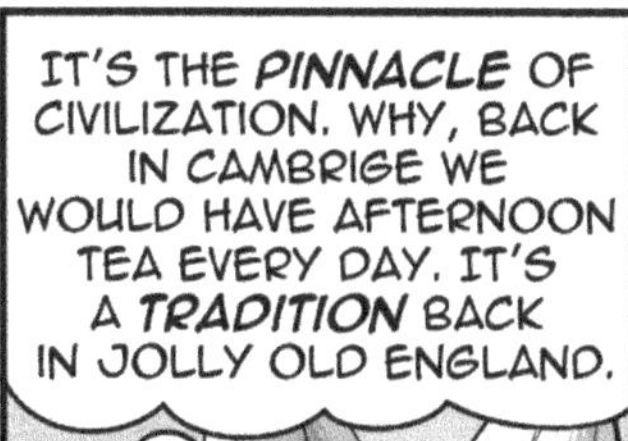

IT'S THE PINNACLE OF CIVILIZATION. WHY, BACK IN CAMBRIGE WE WOULD HAVE AFTERNOON TEA EVERY DAY. IT'S A TRADITION BACK IN JOLLY OLD ENGLAND.

YOU... YOU KNOW WE'RE DOGS, RIGHT?
STUBBY

WHY OF ***COURSE*** I KNOW WE'RE DOGS. BUT, MY GOOD SIR, YOU SIMPLY ***MUST*** TRY A SPOT OF TEA. GET SOME ***CULTURE*** IN YOU.

NONSENSE. A TEA PARTY IS A PERFECTLY RESPECTABLE WAY OF SPENDING AN AFTERNOON WITH FRIENDS.
SMELLS FUNNY.

DON'T YOU ALL LOOK SO PRETTY!!!!

THERE. NOW WE'RE ALL READY FOR THE GUEST OF HONOR!

GUEST OF HONOR?

ALL RISE FOR HER ROYAL MAJESTY, THE QUEEN OF FRANCE.

QUEEN COLETTE!

MORE TEA, YOUR MAJESTY?
NOT. A. WORD.
YOU KNOW WHAT? THIS TEA ISN'T HALF BAD.

IT'S OKAY, I GUESS. BUT YOU KNOW WHAT WOULD REALLY HIT THE SPOT?

WHO WANTS CAKE?

ME!
ME!
ME!

FINE.
SIGH

LET THEM...
...EAT CAKE!

CRACKLE CRACKLE

CRACK!
CRASH!

MON DIEU, COLETTE! MY FAVORITE CHAIR!

THAT'S IT. NO MORE TREATS FOR YOU, MY DEAR LADY.
YOU ARE GOING ON A *DIET*!

DIET?

I AM DEAD...

THIS IS CRIMINAL. THIS IS AN OUTRAGE.
Colette

THIS IS THE *BEST* MEAL I'VE EVER EATEN!
THE BONE IS DIVINE!

Colette

GASTON IS A *GENIUS*!

TORTURE. IT IS *TORTURE*.
Colette

ONCE AGAIN... I AM DEAD.
Colette

OH, MY POOR, POOR STOMACH. HOW LONG HAS IT BEEN SINCE YOU'VE BEEN FED? DAYS? WEEKS? MONTHS?
GROOWWLLL

I MUST FEND FOR MYSELF. I HAVE BECOME SOFT. SPOILED.

I MUST HUNT. LIKE MY ANCESTORS. I WILL NOT BE DENIED SUSTENANCE!

HOW LONG HAS THIS DIET BEEN GOING ON NOW?
ABOUT 45 MINUTES.
A NEW RECORD.
GNAW! GNAW! GNAW!

PIERRE, MY STUPID LITTLE BULLDOG. I WISH TO LEAVE YOU MY FOOD BOWL WHEN I PASS ON.

MAY IT BRING YOU THE SUSTENANCE I WAS DENIED IN THIS LIFE...
Colette

BENSON. I WISH FOR YOU TO HAVE MY CAT SCRATCHER.
IT HAS ALWAYS BROUGHT ME JOY.

UNLIKE THE JOY OF EATING THAT WAS STRIPPED AWAY FROM ME.
Colette

AND TO MY DEAR AMERICAN, STUBBY... SOME ADVICE.
NEVER TRUST A FRENCH MAN. AND NEVER GO ON A DIET.

SHE WAS DEARLY LOVED.
WHY DID SHE HAVE TO BE TAKEN FROM US SO YOUNG???

OH, COLETTE! STOP YOUR DRAMATICS, MY DEAR. YOU ARE UPSETTING THE DOGS.

ARISE, MA PETITE.

COME BACK TO LIFE.

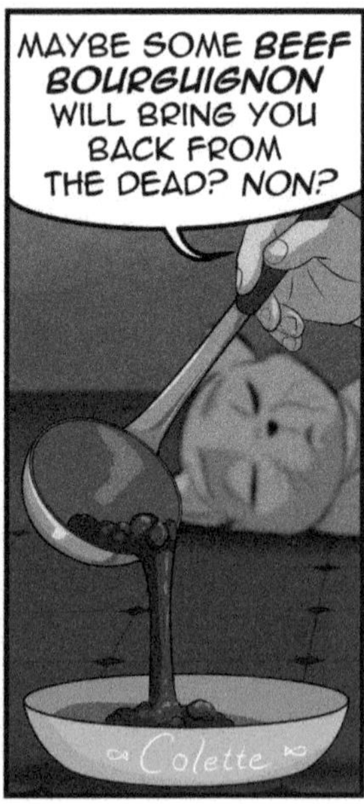
MAYBE SOME BEEF BOURGUIGNON WILL BRING YOU BACK FROM THE DEAD? NON?
Colette

I CANNOT THANK YOU ENOUGH FOR YOUR GENEROUS HOSPITALITY, GASTON.
WHAT AN INCREDIBLE HOME YOU HAVE.
IT WAS OUR PLEASURE, MON AMI.
WE LOVED HAVING YOU AND SERGEANT STUBBY AS OUR GUESTS.

THOUGH, I DON'T KNOW HOW BENSON, PIERRE, AND COLETTE WILL GET ON WITHOUT THEIR AMERICAN FRIEND.

YOU ARE LEAVING?
WHERE ARE YOU GOING?
WAIT... WHAT?
STUBBY
YOU JUST GOT HERE.

WHY WOULD YOU STAY FOR SO SHORT A TIME? I THOUGHT YOU WERE LIVING HERE NOW.
BACK TO AMERICA?
I... I DID, TOO. I GUESS. I DIDN'T KNOW WE WERE GOING HOME AGAIN.

I GUESS SO. I...
STUBBY

I WAS JUST GETTING COMFORTABLE HERE. YOU ALL FELT LIKE... LIKE...
STUBBY

FAMILY.

IT WILL BE GOOD FOR YOU TO RETURN HOME, OLD CHAP. THEY SHALL HAVE PARADES FOR THE CONQUERING WAR HERO... SERGEANT STUBBY!

OH, I DON'T KNOW ABOUT THAT...

NONSENSE! YOU SINGLE-HANDEDLY WON THE WAR!

I WHAT? WHO... WHO SAID I...?
STUBBY

I MAY HAVE EXAGGERATED A BIT REGARDING YOUR EXPLOITS DURING THE WAR.

STUBBY!
TIME TO
GO, PAL.

WELL. I GUESS
THIS IS IT.
STUBBY

SAFE TRAVELS
BACK TO
AMERICA,
MY FRIEND.
THINK OF US
FONDLY WHEN
YOU MARCH IN
YOUR PARADE
IN AMERICA.
EAT LOTS
OF PIZZA
FOR ME.

OKAY, STUBBY.
READY TO SEE
PARIS?
STUBBY

PARIS???

I'VE
ALWAYS
WANTED TO
SEE PARIS!
IT HAS BEEN
SOMETHING OF
A DREAM OF
MINE, AS WELL.
DO THEY
HAVE PIZZA
THERE?

OH, NO NO NO,
YOU THREE. YOU
CANNOT GO
WITH THEM.

THE *NEXT ADVENTURE* FOR THESE TWO MUST BE THEIRS ALONE.

FOR NOW, SAY AU REVOIR TO MY FRIEND *ROBERT* AND HIS REMARKABLE DOG, *SERGEANT STUBBY*!

CPSIA information can be obtained
at www.ICGtesting.com
Printed in the USA
BVHW012106070223
658073BV00013B/270

9 781735 679402